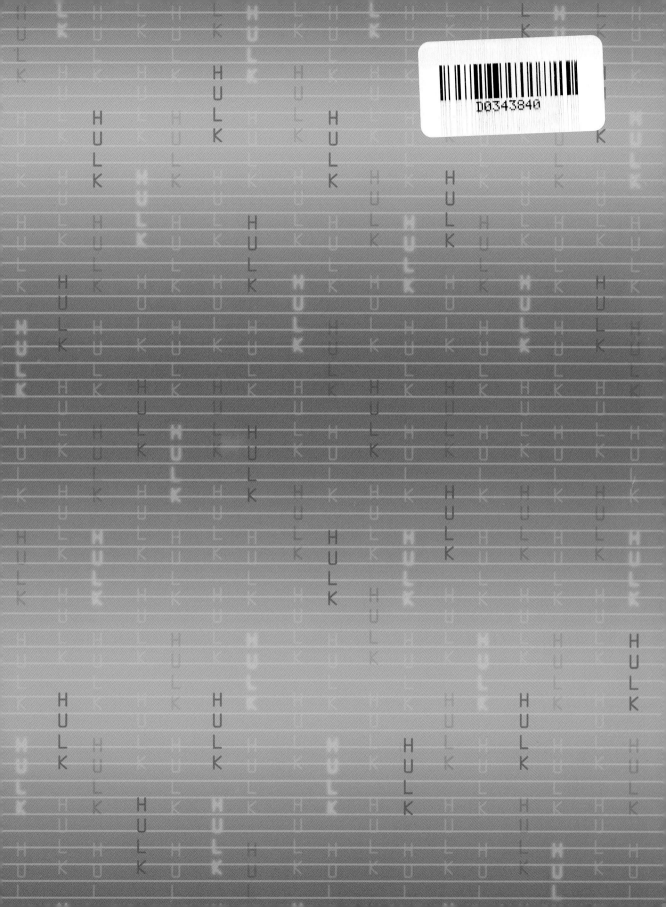

HULK
AN ORIGIN STORY

Bath • New York • Cologne • Melbourne • Delhi
Hong Kong • Shenzhen • Singapore

This edition published by Parragon Books Ltd in 2016

Parragon Books Ltd
Chartist House
15–17 Trim Street
Bath BA1 1HA, UK
www.parragon.com

ISBN 978-1-4748-7705-3

Printed in China

Bruce Banner was not always strong.

He was not always powerful.

And he was not
always able to do
incredible things.

But most of all, Bruce was not always feared.

In fact, when he was young ...

... Bruce was mostly afraid.

He was often sad and
nervous, and he didn't
have a lot of friends.

But he was always ready to help someone in need.

Bruce kept all his feelings
buried deep inside him.

Reading books about science
always took his mind off things.

And so, Bruce spent an awful
lot of time with those books.

As Bruce grew older ...

... he continued to read, study and learn.

But he never learned how
to talk about his feelings.

Bruce became a doctor of science who worked for the army. He worked very hard both day and night.

He was studying a type of energy called gamma radiation.
It was very dangerous, so he needed to be careful when he
was near it. He wanted to find a way to use its power for good.

Bruce decided the best way to test the gamma rays' power was to cause a massive explosion.

He would then measure the dangerous gamma radiation with special equipment.

General 'Thunderbolt' Ross was in charge of the army lab where Bruce worked. He was angry with Bruce. The general had been waiting far too long to find out how much power the gamma rays held.

He needed to know – right now!

But Bruce needed time to make sure the device was safe. He didn't want anyone to get hurt. This made General Ross even angrier, so he yelled at Bruce some more.

Bruce remembered how upset he felt when people yelled at him when he was a kid. So he listened to the general's orders and sent the device to a safe area in the desert to be tested.

Soon, the countdown began.

Suddenly, Bruce noticed something strange
on his computer screen. He looked through his
telescope to see what was wrong.

Someone had driven right into the danger zone!

Bruce rushed out of the lab.

He couldn't let anyone
be hurt by his experiment.

Bruce told the teenager
in the car that he needed to
leave the site right away.

But Bruce quickly realized they
did not have time to clear the area!

He pushed the boy to safety inside a nearby shelter.

5 ... 4 ... 3 ...

2 ... 1 ...

Later, Bruce woke up in an army hospital.
The teenager he had saved was there, too.
Bruce learned the boy's name was Rick Jones.

Rick thanked Bruce for saving his life.

Bruce was happy that Rick was safe.
He was also happy to be alive.

But then, he looked around.
Bruce realized he had been locked up.
He remembered the blast.

Bruce felt so scared, so confused and so helpless ...

... just the way he had when he was young.

He felt trapped.

Just then, something
changed in Bruce.

The soldiers didn't know that the gamma rays
had transformed Bruce! They didn't recognize him.
They called him a HULK!

The army tried to stop the Hulk.
But the Hulk just wanted to leave.

He didn't want to hurt anyone.
He only wanted to be left alone.

So when he noticed that his actions
put the soldiers in harm's way ...

... Hulk knew he needed to help. "HULK SMASH!" he cried.

The Hulk had saved the soldiers!

Then he leaped away before
he could do any more damage.

And not long after ...

... he transformed back into Bruce Banner.

Bruce didn't know if he would ever change
into the Hulk again. He thought it best to hide
out and lay low – just in case.

All the time, he wondered
just how he had become both
a mere man ...

... and The Incredible Hulk.

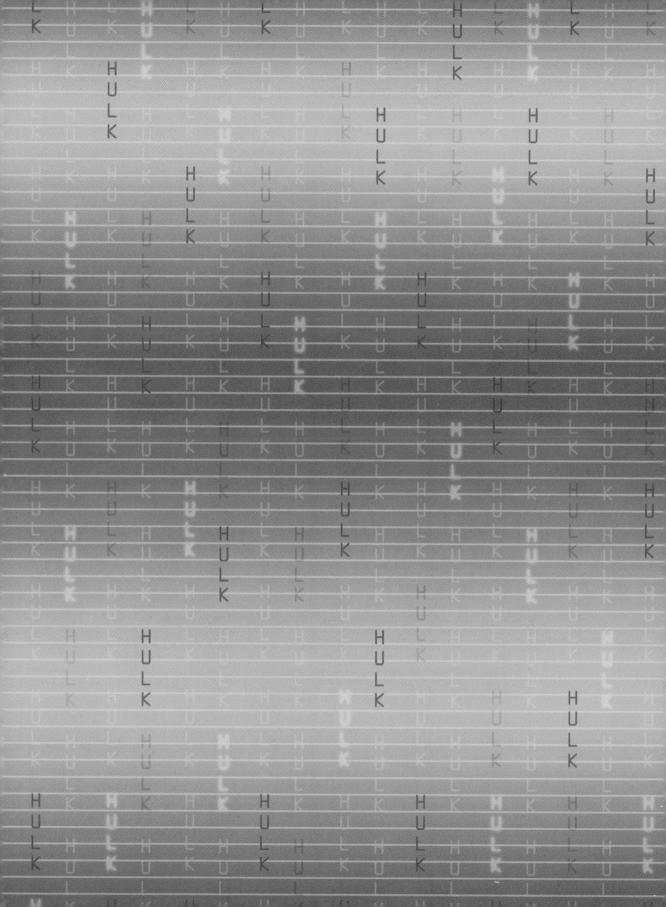